The Wise Bear Stories
Helping you through life's journey

Friendships:
coping with the ups and downs

Scott Cranfield

Illustration Raphilena Bonito

The Wise Bear Stories
Friendships: coping with the ups and downs
Scott Cranfield

Text and Illustration © Scott Cranfield

ISBN 9781912821020

A CIP catalogue record for this book
is available from the British Library.

Published 2019
Tricorn Books
Aspex Gallery, 42 The Vulcan Building
Gunwharf Quays
Portsmouth PO1 3BF

Printed & bound in the UK

Friendships:
coping with the ups and downs

How it Started:

Scott Cranfield the Author of Wise Bear has coached at the highest level for over 30 years, appearing on TV, radio, magazines, as well as hosting multiple seminars and being a key note speaker. His coaching covers subjects from life coaching and family relationships, to sport and business.

Since a young age I have been fascinated with and studied ways to help myself and others live the most inspired and fulfilled life possible. My journey has involved travelling the World attending countless programs and courses covering just about every area of life with the World's leading teachers.

As a father I wanted to share the best of what I had learnt with my children. I found a very effective way of doing this was through bedtime stories. I would create stories involving the challenges and anxieties my children had experienced that day and at the centre of each story is a character called Wise Bear. During the story the children would share with Wise Bear what was upsetting them or causing them to feel anxious. Wise Bear would use his vast experience and wisdom and share a whole new way of looking at these concerns to bring a calming balance to the children's mind, a balance they couldn't find on their own.

In each story the children learn useful tools and actions they can then apply for the rest of their lives.

My whole family are involved in bringing these stories to life, and it is our wish that these stories now help many other children and families, in the way they have helped ours.

Who is Wise Bear:

Wise Bear has been in the same family for generations. He has developed a unique wisdom that allows him to guide children, helping them dissolve their anxieties, as well as helping them make sense of the different challenges and events they experience in their lives. Every story covers a different subject, but within each story Wise Bear offers timeless lessons and vital life skills to help children navigate the journey of their life.

The lessons from Wise Bear will bring a calming balance to your children's mind, and give them a new and empowering perspective on any anxieties or challenges they face.

Even at 100 years old Wise Bear is still fascinated to learn and develop himself. He has had many brilliant teachers along the way, one special one he affectionately refers to as Dr D.

Wise Bear loves to read, exercise, make healthy smoothies and meditate. The only thing that gives away his age are some of his quirky sayings!

More than a story:
Each story ends with an affirmation and a short exercise to reinforce the lesson you have been reading about. This is a great opportunity to work with your children and help them apply the lessons directly to their own life.

Affirmations are a powerful way to develop strong and empowering beliefs for children, and the exercises give the children the opportunity to work through some of the challenges they face, so they can dissolve the anxieties and negative effects they hold in their mind.

Friendships:
coping with the ups and downs

Toby and Alex were excited about their summer holiday. Mum and Dad had booked it months ago, so they had been looking forward to it for ages. When they got there, they weren't disappointed. They were staying in a great hotel, with as much food as they could eat and a huge swimming pool. And of course, Wise Bear had come along too.

On the first day, Toby and Alex grabbed their swimming costumes and towels and rushed to the swimming pool.

"Look at the slide!" Toby gasped. He was staring at the enormous yellow waterslide, where children were squealing with delight as they whooshed down at great speed.

"Race you!" shouted Alex, as she took off, her towel trailing behind her.

They went up and down the waterslide all day, and splashed in the swimming pool.

Alex spotted an inflatable ring and swam towards it. It belonged to a couple of sisters.

"Do you want to play with us?" said one of them.

Alex grinned, happy to have found some other girls to play with. The three girls played for hours.

"Meet you here tomorrow?" Alex said to her new friends.

"Yes!" replied Ellie.

"We can go down the slide together!" Katie said.

Alex was having one of the best holidays ever!
This continued for the next couple of days. Alex and
Toby would get up, grab breakfast, then rush to the
swimming pool. Toby would dart to the slide, and Alex
would find Ellie and Katie and splash around all day.

On the fourth day of the holiday Alex woke up looking
forward to another fun day playing with her friends.

She spotted Ellie at breakfast.

"Hi Ellie, see you at the swimming pool in about half
an hour?" Alex said excitedly.

"No, sorry we can't. We
have to go back to our
room to pack. We're
leaving today to go to
another hotel. It's got an
even bigger slide!"

Ellie rushed off to catch
up with Katie, and
they wolfed down their

breakfast, excited about their new adventure.

Alex was very upset.

"Let's meet up for lunch," Mum said, trying to cheer her up.

Alex attempted a smile.

They all headed towards the swimming pool, Alex dragging her feet and walking a couple of metres behind them. Wise Bear made his excuses and went for a walk in the gardens. He wasn't sure about getting his fur wet – it takes ages to dry.

The family spent the morning playing in the pool together. But after a while, Alex skulked off and lay in the shade on a sunbed. Mum came to keep her company.

At midday, Dad shouted, "Time for lunch everyone!"

Toby clambered out of the pool and grabbed his towel.

"Wise Bear will be there in a moment – hurry up!" Dad reminded Alex, as she slowly got up from the sunbed.

At the restaurant, Dad asked Wise Bear about his walk in the gardens.

"It was quite sensational!" said Wise Bear. "The petunias were magnificent! And the dahlias were something else! How was your morning?"

Mum, Dad and Toby chatted excitedly about the fun they'd had at the pool, the games they'd played and the number of times they'd tackled the slide.

But Alex was very quiet.

"Alex, are you OK?" asked Wise Bear.

Alex sighed.

"I'm feeling sad that I have lost my friends. Ellie and Katie were such good fun and now I don't have anyone," said Alex. "I'm really missing them."

Dad raised his eyebrows and leant towards Wise Bear. "She's been like this all morning. Is there anything you have learnt over the years that could help Alex?"

Wise Bear smiled gently and nodded. "Yes, of course. In fact, this lesson is useful for all of you. Let's order our food and I will share it with you."

The waitress came over and the family ordered their food and drinks. Wise Bear then began his lesson.

"The key message I want to share with you all is learning to ask new questions," said Wise Bear.

"The questions you ask yourself affect the way you feel. So Alex, the problem you face here is in fact an opportunity to ask new questions that will help you feel different."

Dr D always says the quality of the questions you ask determines the quality of your life.

Wise Bear turned directly to Alex.

"Alex, what are you missing from your friends?"

"Just the fact that they were there and now they're not," Alex said, stifling a tear.

"But what specifically about them do you miss? Tell us what it was in particular you liked about them. What was it they did that you feel is absent now?" Wise Bear probed, needing more detailed answers.

Alex thought for a moment, as she fiddled with her cutlery. "There are two things I miss about them. First of all, I miss playing games with them in the swimming pool. And second, I miss chilling with them on the sunbeds."

"OK Alex, that's splendid – much more specific," Wise Bear said. "Now I want you to think and tell me, who has taken their place and is playing games with you in the swimming pool now?"

"Nobody," said Alex firmly. "I haven't met any new friends today."

Wise Bear calmly said again, "In truth, nothing is really ever missing, so who has taken their place?"

Alex, irritated, snapped back at him, "I've told you, my friends are missing; they've gone to another hotel, and I haven't made any new ones."

Alex was getting cross. She felt that Wise Bear wasn't listening and didn't understand how she was feeling. In the meantime, Wise Bear stayed calm. Mum and Dad looked at each other and sighed.

"I do understand that, but let's take a different look at this and hopefully you will see what I mean," Wise Bear persisted.

"You think you are missing friends, so you are looking for more friends. But when you became specific you said you missed playing games in the pool with them. So who has taken their place and is now playing games with you in the swimming pool? In fact, what you're missing doesn't always show up in exactly the same way, so if it's not in the pool it might be some other fun game you are now having with someone."

"Dad played with you," Toby piped up.

Alex scowled at him, but then reflected for a moment.

"Well actually Dad did play with me after breakfast" she conceded. "We played in the pool and a little bat and ball."

Wise Bear carried on with his questions. "And what was better about playing games with your Dad compared to your friends?"

Alex's eyes widened as she replied,

"When I play games with Dad I'm always in the game – I don't have to wait for anybody else."

"Splendid!" said Wise Bear. "What else?"

"With Dad, I'm either jumping off his shoulders or swimming through his legs or playing catch, there is no waiting around, but sometimes with my friends I had to wait a while to join in."

"Spiffing work!" said Wise Bear, getting excited that Alex was understanding the lesson. "Now let's keep going."

Alex was perking up, much to the relief of Mum and Dad.

"What else is better about playing games with Dad compared to your friends?"

"Actually, the games are a bit more exciting because with Dad I get to play games I can't do with my friends."

Wise Bear was nodding knowingly. He looked at Alex with his warm, caring eyes.

"Can you now see that what you thought was missing is still there; it's just happening with Dad instead of your friends. And there are benefits to the way Dad plays with you compared to your friends?"

Alex's face lit up and she replied, "Yes I can! That's amazing! So nothing is ever missing?"

"That's right, Alex," confirmed Wise Bear, holding out his paw to her.

Alex held on to it firmly, as Wise Bear's lesson sunk in.

"That's a lovely lesson, Wise Bear," said Mum, relieved that Alex seemed to be rescued from her sulk.

Wise Bear smiled kindly. "Alex, you also said you missed chilling with your friends on the sunbeds, so who has taken their place?"

Alex had got the hang of these questions so was quick to answer.

"Oh, that was Mum, we laid on the sunbeds next to each other."

"And how is it better chilling with Mum compared to your friends?" asked Wise Bear.

"Actually, it's better because when I'm speaking to Mum, she really listens. My friends often interrupted me."

Alex was beginning to understand that nothing really was missing it just changed to a new form, and that the new form had many benefits compared to the old form.

However, a dark cloud suddenly seemed to cross her face. She looked concerned.

"But I did also enjoy playing and chilling with Ellie and Katie!"

Alex was worried that by answering Wise Bear's questions she was being disloyal to her friends.

Wise Bear smiled kindly.

"I am sure you did! What I want you to gain from this lesson is that because you were only focused on the positives of these friendships, you felt sad when it was missing. But in truth, no friendship has only positives – in which case it is wise to appreciate both the positives and the negatives. This will help keep you balanced and less emotional if anything changes."

Alex looked into Wise Bear's kind eyes. She could see that he was really trying to help her.

"By asking good quality questions we can discover both sides of something and this helps to balance our mind, which generally means you will have longer-lasting and more stable friendships.

"The questions we have used today have helped you realise that nothing is really ever missing – it just changes its form. Good quality questions help us find the new form and its benefits. And this helps to balance our mind."

Alex nodded slowly, as she listened intently.

"So in this situation, Alex, it doesn't mean you enjoyed playing with your friends any less, it just means instead of leaving your mind stuck and only looking at what's missing, you have asked questions to find the new form and the benefits of the new form."

"Does that mean I can enjoy both then?" Alex asked tentatively.

"It most certainly does," Wise Bear said reassuringly.

Wise Bear, sensing Alex's mood was shifting gave a moment or two before asking how she was now feeling.

"I really feel much better. It's almost like I feel lighter

and have more energy," she replied. "I also feel very thankful to Mum and Dad."

"Jolly good show, Alex!" said Wise Bear.

"Thank you, Wise Bear," said Dad.

The lesson finished just in time. The waitress brought over their lunch and they all eagerly tucked in. There was a new energy and they chatted all the way through their meal.

When they had finished, Mum said, "Now who would like an ice cream?"

There was a loud chorus of "Yes! Me!"

These new questions really helped Alex enjoy the rest of her holiday. Of course, she met more new friends at the hotel, but this time if they weren't there one day, she had a whole different mindset. Thanks to Wise Bear's lesson, she found opportunity in each situation.

Wise Bear Affirmation: What you say to yourself can make a big difference to how you think.
That's why Wise Bear always recommends an affirmation to help you remember his stories.
Here is today's one…

"New questions can give me a new life."

Wise Bear recommends repeating these affirmations regularly. You can say them either out loud or inside your head.

Wise Bear exercise:

Use the questions below to discuss with your children and family how Wise Bear thinking can help you.

Use the chart below to think of 10 occasions when you felt like you were missing something or had lost something and then see if you can find the new form, and what the benefits were of this new form.

Here are two examples to start you off:

What's lost or missing?	What do you miss about this?	The new form	Benefit to the new form
Your favourite watch	It made me feel smart	Since losing my watch I have taken more care to look after my clothes, so I look smart	Now my overall experience is smart rather than just a watch. Mum is also pleased with me that I'm looking after my clothes more.
My bicycle – it was stolen, and we can't afford a new one yet	The excitement of riding	My friend's spare bike. I get to use this when I go to their house	My friend's bike is bigger than mine which is better for me as I have grown taller

What's lost or missing?	What do you miss about this?	The new form	Benefit to the new form

What's lost or missing?	What do you miss about this?	The new form	Benefit to the new form